THE FOX IN THE WOOD

About the Author

Rosemary Hayes lives and works in East Anglia. She has written several information books for children and her first children's novel, RACE AGAINST TIME, was runner-up for the Kathleen Fidler Award in 1987.

THE FOX IN THE WOOD

A Wartime Adventure

by Rosemary Hayes

Anglia Young Books

First published in 1989
by Anglia Young Books
Durhams Farmhouse, Ickleton
Saffron Walden, Essex CB10 1SR

Illustrations by Tessa Hamilton

Design and production in association with
Book Production Consultants
47 Norfolk Street
Cambridge CB1 2LE

British Library Cataloguing in Publication Data
Hayes, Rosemary
  The fox in the wood.
  I. Title
  823'.914 [J]

ISBN 1-871173-02-7

Typeset in 10½/12½ point Palatino by Witwell Ltd, Southport
and printed in Great Britain by
Redwood Burn Ltd, Trowbridge, Wiltshire

AUTHOR'S NOTE

THE FOX IN THE WOOD is not a true story but it is based on the experiences of the many people who have been kind enough to talk to me about village life in East Anglia during World War Two. I am indebted to them all.

The aim of the book is to give modern children some idea of what ordinary village life was like during those years and to show them how the war affected everything – school life, home life, what you wore, what you ate, where you went and what you did.

CHAPTER ONE

Everyone knew that war was coming.

It was September 1st 1939 and I stood shivering on a London railway station, amongst hundreds and hundreds of other children. Mum had written my name and address on a label and sewn it onto my coat and, like everyone else, I had a gas-mask, in its cardboard box, hung round my neck.

We kept getting jostled by the crowd and I held Mum's hand very tightly. The train had been waiting for ages, belching and hissing, and everywhere ladies were forming people into lines, trying to keep schoolchildren together, shouting and pointing.

Then, at last, the children from my school were told to get on. Gently, Mum prized her hand away from mine:
'Go on, love. On you get.'
She wiped her hand across her eyes and sniffed:
'Go *on*, Annie love. Look, all the other children are getting on. You'll be alright. You'll be near your friends.'
I couldn't move. I didn't want to go anywhere. I wanted to stay with Mum. My lip trembled and hot tears of misery ran down my face:
'Please let me stay!' I sobbed, trying to hold onto her. But somehow, she got me, struggling, onto the train and into the charge of my teacher, then she fought her way back through the crowds and out of my sight.

I was only eight years old – and I'd never been so unhappy in my life.

But this was war – and even eight-year-old girls were caught up in it. People called World War 2 "the most expected war in history". Everyone had been making preparations for months.

Leaflets kept coming to our little house in Tottenham, leaflets from the Government telling us about our gas masks, our food, what to do in an air-raid, how to black out our windows and, of course, about evacuation. Evacuation meant sending children away from the big towns to safety in the country.

At first, evacuation had sounded fun.
'It'll be like a holiday,' said Mum. 'A holdiay in the country.'
I'd never been to the country. I couldn't imagine what the country was like.
Then our teacher at school had made it sound exciting, too:
'I shall be coming with you,' she said. 'They'll try and keep you together.'
We'd just got a different teacher. She was an old lady who had been asked to come back and help out. Our usual teacher had gone off to do some special war work.

Nearly all the grown-ups were doing some war work and a lot of the men had joined the armed forces. My dad had already gone away. Those men who were too old or unfit to fight were doing other war jobs. Lots of them were ARP (Air Raid Precaution) wardens who helped the ordinary people get ready for war.

The ARP wardens had even organised a mock air-raid in our street. We had blacked out our windows and when the siren sounded we all pretended that bombs were falling from the sky.

It had been good fun. Everyone had laughed and joked and afterwards the children had played war games in the street.

But as I sat hunched beside this teacher I hardly knew, all that seemed a long way away, and evacuation was no fun at all.

The train hadn't left. There were crowds of people still on the platform. I peered out of the window.

I heard a shout – louder than all the other shouting – and saw a large lady telling people to get out of her way. She was pulling behind her a big flat wooden trolley, on which sat about a dozen children – they were even younger than me. I stared at them as they passed my window. They looked completely bewildered.

The carriage was packed with children from our school. We all came from poor homes and, now I think about it, we must have been a scruffy lot. I know that at home we didn't have running water in the house – just a tap out in the back garden – so it wasn't very easy to keep clean.

All the other children seemed quite cheerful. I was really cross to see that Tommy Baxter was in the same carriage. He was big and noisy and kept teasing the girls. He was talking to the teacher:
'Please miss, where are we going?'
He sniffed and wiped his nose on his sleeve.
The teacher looked at him:
'Not far from Cambridge, Tommy. But I can't tell you exactly where. You will be found homes in nearby villages.'

And with that we had to be content.

At last the train moved slowly out of the station. I watched miserably as we passed row upon row of grimy terraced houses, most of them with sandbags against the windows to protect them from bomb-blasts. Everyone said that London would be the main target. That's why we were being sent to the country.

In the corridor of the train, I saw a mother with her two young children. The toddler was clinging to her skirts while the baby was screaming. The poor woman paced up and down with the baby over her shoulder, trying to comfort it.

The train seemed very slow, but gradually the houses gave way to fields. All of us town children looked out in wonder.
'Hey,' said Tommy, 'look at the cows!'

As we travelled further north, we saw more cornfields – some being harvested and some neatly cut down to stubble. At the time, I'd never thought about where bread came from; so far as I was concerned, it came from the baker's shop. In the months ahead, I was to learn a lot about country life.

We were all tired and hungry and thirsty when our teacher said:
'Now children. Listen to me. In a few minutes, we shall reach Cambridge. You must get ready to get off the train.'

Up till then, I had just felt numb. Now, I really started to panic.

Children started to stand up, one by one, including Tommy Baxter.

'Please don't let me go to the same place as Tommy,' I thought.

Slowly, I got out of my seat and reached up for the battered suitcase Mum had found for me. I stared out of the window as the train juddered to a halt.

'Stop gawping, Annie Foster,' said a voice behind me, but I was so miserable I couldn't answer. Tommy Baxter gave me a shove:
'Come on, get a move on or we'll all be left behind.'

Moments later, we had all scrambled off the train onto the platform – a herd of tired, dirty, scruffy town children. There were a lot of people there to meet us – ordinary men and women, ARP wardens, ladies with lists and someone who introduced himself as the Billeting Officer. He and our teacher talked anxiously while we children stood closely together, staring about us.

Everyone was staring at us, too. It was horrible; we felt like animals in a zoo.

I felt a lump in my throat. It was all so strange, and I missed my Mum. Then I heard a voice behind me:
'Don't snivel, or no-one'll take you!' said Tommy.
I wiped my eyes and turned round. I poked my tongue out at him. At that moment, I hated Tommy Baxter more than anything else in the world.

It took a long time before we were all sorted out. Gradually, my friends melted away, in the company of other grown-ups. I was in the last group to go – so was Tommy. But at last we were loaded onto a bus with our luggage. There were a couple of busy looking ladies with us and our teacher.

'Where are we going now?' I whispered.

Our teacher smiled: 'It's not much further, Annie. This group is going to a village south of Cambridge.'

But it *was* much further. The bus chugged slowly along the country roads, twisting and turning. I started to feel sick. I felt too ill to bother to look at the countryside. I could only think of Mum and our house in Tottenham.

At last the bus stopped in a village street and we got out, even more tired, hungry and dirty than before. We were met by another Billeting Officer and each of us was given special emergency rations. Every evacuee had enough food to keep him or her going for two days, and this had to be given to the families who were going to look after us.

Then the Billeting Officer marched us all down the village street. He knocked at cottage doors as he went and asked the people inside how many children they could take. No-one seemed pleased to see us; except for one lady. She already had a mass of children of her own, but she smiled and opened her arms:
'Poor little things! I'll take as many as I can.'

But the other villagers took in children very unwillingly, scowling at our dirty faces, scruffy clothes and untidy hair. Tommy was placed with a hard-faced woman who argued with the Billeting Officer:
'Why do we have to have these filthy vermin-ridden children in our clean houses?' she shouted.

The Billeting Officer was calm, but firm:
'You know it's Government orders', he said quietly.

She bundled Tommy inside and slammed the door.

I was beginning to hope that no-one would want me

and I could go home to Mum.

But then my luck changed. An old battered car drove up the village street and a middle-aged couple got out and hurried over to the Billeting Officer.

'Oh dear, I'm so sorry we're late. Trouble with the sheep,' said the woman.
Then she pointed to me:
'Is this little one for us? Can we have her?'
The Billeting Officer nodded and I burst into tears.
Then I felt myself hugged in strong capable arms and smothered by a smell I didn't recognise – a smell of sheep and dung and straw and hay; an indefinable country smell.

Mrs Wimpole held me away from her and, fishing out a hankie from her pocket, she gently wiped my tears and blew my nose for me. Her husband stood behind her and beamed down at me.

• • • • •

Mr and Mrs Wimpole told me that they had a farm just outside the village:
'We were so late, we brought the car,' said Mr Wimpole, as he piled me into it with my luggage. 'Usually we walk down.'
'We thought you'd be tired, too,' said Mrs Wimpole.

It was very quiet as we chugged up the hill. No noisy traffic, no people. Just birds and animals. I sat in front, on Mrs Wimpole's lap. Mr Wimpole took his hand off the wheel and pointed to a small concrete hut near the top of the hill:
'See, Ann, we're all ready for the war.'
'What is it?' My voice was only a whisper. I was very shy.

'That's a pillbox,' he replied. Then he went on:
'That's for a machine-gun if the Germans come.'
'Oh hush, John,' said Mrs Wimpole. 'She's far too young to bother about all that. Let her be, poor child.' Then she squeezed me:
'What do they call you at home – Ann or Annie?'
'Mum calls me Annie,' I said, the lump coming back to my throat.
'Well, Annie. We'll have some tea, and then I'll show you the farm.'

• • • • •

On September 1st 1939, the day I arrived at the Wimpoles' farm, Hitler's troops invaded Poland. Two days later, the British Prime Minister, Mr Neville Chamberlain, announced over the radio (or wireless, as we called it) "we are now at war with Germany."

And so, as an eight-year-old Londoner, I settled down to live on the Wimpoles' farm in an East Anglian village just south of Cambridge. Little did I know then that I would spend so long there or that I would play a very special – and secret – part in the war.

CHAPTER TWO

To begin with, I found country life very strange. I was used to city dirt, but not squelchy mud and sheep dung.

The moment I arrived at the farm, Mrs Wimpole looked at my feet squashed into my best shoes.

'Ah,' she said, smiling. 'I thought as much.' She went to a cupboard and brought something out.
'Look, Annie. I keep spare wellington boots here. There are all sorts of sizes. They belonged to my two boys when they were small.'
She sighed: 'I wish they were still small. But they're grown-up now and they've both joined the forces. They can't wait to go to war.'

I'd never worn wellington boots. We didn't need them in Tottenham. I thought they looked ugly and clumsy. My face fell. Mrs Wimpole smiled. She led me to the window.
'If you are going to see round the farm dear, you can't wear your London shoes,' she said gently.

I saw what she meant. It had rained recently and there was still a lot of mud about – and lots of straw and long grass.

As she was getting tea, she told me about the other people who lived on the farm.

'You're not the only Londoner here, Annie,' she said. 'We've got three young women from London, working on the farm for us.'

'What are they doing?' I asked.

'Well, it's their war work. They've volunteered to join something called The Land Army. They're helping with the harvest now, and I hope they'll stay on. You see, our farm workers and our sons have gone away to fight. And we can't manage this place by ourselves.'

Mrs Wimpole was spreading big thick slices of bread with margerine. She laughed:

'You should have seen them when they arrived. All dressed up in their London clothes. The first day they refused to wear the special clothes they'd been issued.'

'What sort of clothes?'

'Oh – good strong shoes, wellington boots and dungarees.'

'So, what happened?'

'Well, my husband was a bit naughty. He made them go and spread dung on the stubble. They had to load up the horse and cart from the dung-heap, then shovel the dung out from the back of the cart all over the field! After that, they soon saw the sense of wearing sensible clothes!'

I smiled then. Probably for the first time since I'd left Mum.

Mrs Wimpole saw the smile. She said:

'They're lovely girls, Annie. You'll like them. They've settled in really well. We couldn't do without them.'

• • • • •

She was right. I did like them; I met them when they came in for tea, hot and tired, but cheerful. The kitchen rang with laughter and they told me all the mistakes they had made:

'You'll soon get used to it, Annie,' said one.

'Have you ever seen a sheep?' asked another.
I shook my head.
'Well, I was scared stiff of them at first. But you don't
need to be. They're silly creatures.'

When Mrs Wimpole was out of the room, one of them said:

'I wish there was something to do in the evenings. There's no pictures, no dance-halls; it's pretty boring. Not like London.'

'There's not so much to do in London now,' said another.

'Everything's closing down. Everyone's doing war-work. I'm glad I'm here. The food's good, too.'

'Yes. But they say that's going to change. Food's going to be rationed soon.'

After tea, Mrs Wimpole took me round the farm. I was frightened of the animals – the sheep and the carthorses – but I liked the chickens. Mrs Wimpole let me help collect the eggs.

'I tell you what, Annie,' she said. 'When you've settled in, you can have a job, too. You can feed the chickens in the evenings, after school, and collect the eggs.'

I smiled again. Despite everything, I was going to enjoy my time in the country.

Not all my friends had been so lucky.

• • • • •

Like all the other children from London, I had to go to the village school. The first day, Mrs Wimpole walked down the hill with me to show me where it was. She took me over to my friends, gave me a hug, and said: 'Come straight back to the farm after school Annie. And don't forget your gas-mask.'

We weren't allowed anywhere without our gas-masks. They were a real nuisance. Even though some of us younger children had special "Mickey Mouse" masks, we soon got fed up with them.

'Why do we have them, anyway?' I asked Mrs Wimpole. 'Well dear, in the last war, the Germans used a horrible poisonous gas. They might use it again. So your mask is important. Don't forget it!'

I was soon chatting with the other London children.
'What's your place like?' they asked me. I was the only one who wasn't right in the village.
'Really nice,' I said. 'What about yours?'
Some of them said they were OK. Some of them said they were awful.
'The village children say no-one wanted to have us. That Billeting Officer man made them.'
'Yes, I heard that, too.'
'What do you do in the evenings?' I asked.
'Listen to Children's Hour on the wireless. Play games. It's not bad. But I wish I was back in London.'

Tommy Baxter seemed to have come off worst:
'She's got a real temper, the mother,' he said. 'We've got the lady who was with us on the train – the one with two little children. She's in the house, too. The mother moans all the time about sharing her kitchen with another woman.'

It was hard for everyone. The village people, having to share their homes with strangers – and the Londoners, taken from their homes and often put with families who didn't want them.

The bell rang and we all filed into the little school. There were more London children than village children and to start with we were very suspicious of each other.

Gradually, though, school life settled down. Each day we would have gas-mask drill, when we raced to see who could get their mask on quickest, and several times a week we had shelter drill.

A public air-raid shelter had been built on the recreation ground just near the school. It had a big white "S" painted on it. When the time came for shelter drill, we all put on our coats, took our gas-masks, and trooped across the recreation ground to the shelter where we sat on wooden benches in the damp half-light and sniffed disinfectant.

But, for me, the best moment of the day was when we were released from school, with: 'Don't forget your gas-masks,' and I ran up the hill to the farm, dumped my gas-mask and school bag on the kitchen table and went out to feed the chickens and collect the eggs.

'You're turning into a real country girl,' said Mr Wimpole one day.
'I like the chickens,' I said.
'Would you like to shut them up at night, too? Look after them completely? Check if any of them is sick?'
'Yes please!' I felt really important.

• • • • •

I soon settled into my life in the country. Mum came to visit me as often as she could, but she was busy now doing war-work in London.

'Everyone's doing something,' she said. 'Your Auntie's got a job at an aircraft factory. She has to wear dungarees and cover her hands with grease before she starts work!'

I laughed: 'Not Auntie Madge!'

My Auntie Madge was very pretty and very fussy. I couldn't imagine her covered with grease.

Mum could see that I was happy and Mrs Wimpole always gave her a few eggs to take back to London.

• • • • •

During the early months of the war, nothing dramatic happened. There were no bombs but, slowly, ordinary things changed.

First, there was rationing. Ration books had been issued at the end of September 1939, but nothing was rationed until January 1940. Some of the first things to be rationed were bacon and ham (4 oz per person per week) and sugar (12 oz per person per week). Soon after, bread, eggs, butter, meat and sweets were all rationed, and so was soap. I'd been used to eating sweets all the time in London. Now they became a treat.

There were only a few coupons in the ration books for sweets. Once you'd used up your ration for the week, there were no more to be had.

People working on a farm were allowed a little extra at the busy times – harvest, haymaking, sugarbeet lifting – and Mrs Wimpole had the job of dividing up the extra rations fairly between everyone.

The most exciting thing to happen, in those early months, was when some men appeared at school and started to cut down the iron railings at the front of the building. All us children stared in amazement, but the teachers told us the metal would be made into weapons.

A lot of the London evacuees went home after a month or two. There were no bombs and they missed their families. But I stayed on and so did a handful of others, among them Tommy Baxter.

It was a very hard winter, the winter of 1939/40. As I

trudged up the hill after school, I was glad that there was a warm fire waiting for me. One day Mrs Wimpole met me and, for once, she looked really cross:

'Annie. Do you know what I've just heard?'

'What?'

'We've been told that it is an offence to feed wild birds in winter!'

'Why?'

'I suppose its counted as a waste of food.'

'Will you stop feeding the robins, then?'

'Certainly not. They aren't at war!'

• • • • •

And so the war dragged on. Every night, the Wimpoles listened to the news bulletins on the wireless but I never took much notice. Just so long as no bombs dropped on Mum or on me I didn't mind. Things got scarcer, but that was all.

Every day we went through the same drills at school and every evening we put up the blackouts at the farm windows before we lit the lamps. There were occasional air-raid warnings, when we pushed the big table against the window and hid underneath it. But, on the whole, it was all very quiet and peaceful. So far, the bombs had done no real damage in the area.

In May 1940 Winston Churchill became Prime Minister.

Then, on June 19th, 1940, two bombs fell on Cambridge – only a few miles away. Ten people were killed and a dozen injured.

Suddenly, the war was real – and on our doorstep.

CHAPTER THREE

After that, we were all much more nervous. Up until that moment, no-one in the village had felt in any real danger, but now every family made sure they'd done everything possible to protect themselves. At the farm, we had a bucket of sand outside every building, with a ladder and rake standing beside it. The sand was to smother incendiary bombs (bombs designed to cause fire) and the ladder and rake would be used to remove unexploded bombs that might land on the roof.

Mrs Wimpole decided that it was too risky to rely on the heavy kitchen table for protection and she said it was time we had a proper air-raid shelter at the farm, so Mr Wimpole was sent off, grumbling, to look for one. But he returned empty handed:
'£7.10s (£7.50) each!' he said. 'And we'd need at least two. That's far too expensive. I can make a better job of it myself.'

So, he and two of the Land Army girls reinforced the roof and sides of one of the small farm sheds and Mrs Wimpole put bedding and a few emergency rations in it.

Mr Wimpole grinned as he stood back to admire his work: 'That's a lot better than anything we could buy!'

We had our own farm hoses which were always connected to a water supply, so that they could be used to fight a fire if necessary. Down in the village, the ARP wardens went from house to house, making sure that everyone knew where the nearest stirrup pump was kept – this was a special portable water pump that could be used to extinguish a small fire.

Everywhere there was activity. The village had several ARP wardens, and they became a familiar sight. They didn't have a uniform – just a silver badge, wellington boots, a tin hat, a whistle and a bell. They often practised fire-fighting or first-aid with the Home Guard (local men too old to fight but who were trained to protect the village in case of an invasion). Once, the head of the Home Guard, who was a retired army officer, organised a mock invasion of the village. All us children had to stay inside the school and lie on the floor while the Home Guard and the ARP wardens got rid of the "enemy"!

In Cambridge, there were proper sirens ("Moaning Minnies" they were called) that went off to warn people of an air raid. But, in our village, we had no siren. Cambridge would telephone the ARP warden on duty to say that the siren had gone. Then, he would get on his bike and pedal round the village blowing a whistle. This was the signal for everyone to take shelter. When Cambridge told him that the "All Clear" siren had gone, he would get on his bike again and go round the village ringing his bell!

Most of the ARP wardens were very good and remembered to telephone the farm so that we knew when to take shelter, too, but sometimes they forgot!

• • • • •

It was about this time that something odd happened at the farm. I had been feeding the chickens after school one day and as I came back towards the house I happened to look up. My eye caught a movement and I saw a shadow cross one of the attic windows – someone was there. I frowned. Who could it be? It was market day and Mr and Mrs Wimpole were both in Saffron Walden. All the Land Army girls were working outside – I'd just passed them.

There was no-one else on the farm.

In the evening I mentioned it to Mrs Wimpole and she replied crossly:
'Don't be silly Annie. There's no-one else here. Now help me set the table.'

I said no more at the time, but I kept thinking about that shadow. I *had* seen it. It wasn't my imagination.

• • • • •

All the village women were "doing their bit" towards the war effort. They turned their gardens into vegetable plots, they repaired old clothes, they saved anything that could be used again. There were posters everywhere – "Dig for Victory", "Up Housewives and at 'em" were just two of them. And I remember a rhyme we used to recite: "Little scraps of paper, Little bits of tin, Make up into weapons, Help our men to win."

Mrs Wimpole was always busy – either at the farm or in the village. When it was playtime at school, I often saw her coming out of one particular house.

'What do you do there?' I asked her one day.

'Oh, that's our knitting group, Annie,' she said. 'We

meet most days, for an hour or so, and we knit "comforts" for the troops.'

'Comforts?'

'Yes – socks, gloves, balaclavas – things like that. Perhaps you'd like to come and do some in the holidays?'

I shook my head: 'I can't knit.'

'Never mind. There's plenty else you could do. You could write out labels, sew up seams. And, if you like, I could teach you to knit at home, in the evenings.'

She was as good as her word, and soon I had knitted my very first scarf!

One weekend, Mrs Wimpole said:
'Annie. There's a job I'd like you to do.'
'What's that?'
'I'd like you to check all the window panes in the house. Just make sure they still have tape across them.'

Sticky tape had been put across all the windows to stop them shattering from bomb-blasts, but it had been done right at the beginning of the war, and some of the tape had peeled off. It took me the whole of Saturday to go round every window in the house with my roll of sticky tape, and when I thought I'd finished, I remembered the attic windows.

I hesitated. I didn't want to go up to the attic; the memory of that shadowy figure was too strong.

But Mrs Wimpole had said there was no-one there.

I swallowed, then slowly mounted the tiny attic staircase. I'd never been up there before. At the top of the stairs was a small door. My hands were damp with perspiration and I wiped them down the side of my dress before I tried the handle. Very slowly and quietly, I turned it.

The door was locked.

My heart started to beat faster. Why was the door locked? What was inside? I knelt down and peered through the keyhole. The attic was large and full of old cases which had been carefully stacked on one side of the room. On the other side, I could just see a made up bed, a marble-topped washstand with a bowl and jug on top, and a bedside table. There was a chair too, with a man's shirt hanging over it and under the bed was a pair of bedroom slippers.

Mrs Wimpole had lied to me; there *was* someone else in the house!

I went downstairs slowly and found Mrs Wimpole in the kitchen. I sat down at the table and drew patterns on the wood with my finger.
'What's the matter, Annie?' said Mrs Wimpole.
I blushed: 'Nothing.'
Mrs Wimpole stopped what she was doing and looked at me:
'I know you too well Annie. Something's worrying you; what is it?'
I hung my head:
'I went up to the attic to do the windows,' I whispered.
She looked up sharply and, for the first time since I'd known her, she looked embarrassed.
'Oh dear,' she said. 'I'd forgotten you'd go up there.' She stopped to take some bread out of the oven, then she wiped her hands carefully on her apron and sat down heavily on a chair beside me. She took one of my hands in hers:

'What did you see?' she asked quietly.

I blushed again:

'The door was locked but I looked through the keyhole. I saw the bed made up and a man's shirt and slippers and things.'

Mrs Wimpole sighed:

'Well,' she said, almost to herself, 'I suppose I couldn't keep him hidden for ever.'

'Now Annie,' she went on, 'you must listen carefully. This is important.'

I nodded.

I'm afraid I lied to you the other day. We *have* got another visitor. He's a relation of ours and we call him Uncle Bob.'

'How long's he going to stay?' I asked.

Mrs Wimpole frowned: 'I don't know, Annie. Some time, I expect.' She looked across at me.

'I want you to forget what you saw in the attic, Annie. I don't want you talking about Uncle Bob. Not to anyone. Not even to the other girls. Only Mr Wimpole and I know that he's here. I'm going to have to trust you, dear. You mustn't say a word. Do you understand?'

I'd never heard Mrs Wimpole talk like that. I felt a shiver at the back of my neck.

'Yes,' I whispered.

She nodded, as if satisfied.

'You remember what the poster says, "Careless talk costs lives". Well, if you tell anyone about Uncle Bob – your school friends, their parents, anyone – it could be very serious. You never know who they may tell or who else may be listening.'

There was silence for a minute or two, then I plucked up my courage:

'Is he doing something secret for the war?' I asked.

'That's not your business, Annie,' said Mrs Wimpole. 'Now remember, I'm trusting you to keep quiet about him.'

'But what if I bring a school friend back to tea?' I asked. Teas at the farm were always popular with my friends; Mrs Wimpole was very generous. She knew that most of the remaining London evacuees (and the village children) had less to eat than we did on the farm. She would often send them back with a few eggs to help the household.

Mrs Wimpole laughed and ruffled my hair:
'Don't worry about that Annie. Uncle Bob won't show himself. He's good at keeping out of the way.'

That night I dreamt about Uncle Bob. It was a horrible dream. He was chasing me up the attic stairs; they went on and on and I could never reach the top. Just as he was about to grab me from behind I woke up, trembling with fright.

• • • • •

The next morning, I had a letter from Mum:
'All your talk about eggs and chickens makes me really jealous,' she wrote. 'We poor folk in the towns are only allowed one egg every week. I'll come and see you as soon as I can, but things are difficult here – and the trains don't run very regularly now ...'

I thought, every day, of Mum and my other relations squashed into our tiny house in Tottenham. I still missed her terribly, but even so, I didn't really want to go back now.

We felt the shortages, too, but not so badly as people in towns. We had vegetables and eggs, and families joined

25

together to form a "pig club", saving scraps to feed up a pig, then sharing it between them. We often ate rabbit, too. They bred quickly and were tasty, but I hated to see them all in their hutches and know they were going to end up on the table.

But no-one had much of anything that had to be brought in from abroad. Oranges and bananas were things of the past, and coffee and tea were becoming very scarce.

'In the autumn, Annie, I'll send you out picking rose-hips,' said Mrs Wimpole.

'What for?'

'Rose-hip tea,' she said. Then she laughed: 'We'll never last on our tea ration, the way my husband drinks the stuff.'

• • • • •

But all thoughts of my Mum – and even about the mysterious Uncle Bob – were put right out of my head one afternoon. It was towards the end of the summer term; the corn was high and the sun shone warm on my back as I walked up the farm track. I hummed to myself and chewed a piece of grass.

Suddenly, I was aware of a shadow, then a rushing sound. I looked up and saw almost above me an aeroplane, on fire, with smoke billowing out behind it. It screamed towards the earth and it seemed as though it would hit me. I couldn't move. I remember saying, over and over again: 'Please don't hit me. Please don't hit me.'

Then it crashed, with a sickening thud, followed by an explosion. It landed only one field away from me. At last, I moved. I ran, then, as fast as I could, up the track, round to the back door of the farmhouse:

'Mr Wimpole! Mr Wimpole! Come quick.'

But Mr Wimpole had already seen it. He was running from the other direction, towards the house.

'Alright Annie,' he panted. 'Run and get the big map. You'll be quicker than me.'

I knew what he meant. The nearby airfield of Duxford had issued a map showing all the surrounding land divided into numbered sections. It was kept in Mr Wimpole's study. I rushed into the study and picked it up off the desk, then ran into the hall.

Mr Wimpole was already ringing Duxford Airfield. I opened up the map for him and he pointed to the field where the 'plane had crashed.

'I haven't got my glasses, Annie. What's the number?'

I told him, and he told the people at Duxford.

He put the 'phone down.

'They'll send someone right away,' he said. 'But I'd better go down to the 'plane and see if there's anything I can do.'

'Can I come too?' I asked.

He patted my head: 'No Annie. You've been a great help already. You stay here and tell Mrs Wimpole what's happened when she comes in.'

I watched from the top of the drive. It was only a few minutes before the Air Force jeep arrived from the airfield together with a fire engine and, before long, there was no sign of smoke or fire. After a while, the 'plane was cordoned off and all the people went away, except one man who was left behind to guard it.

'Was it one of ours?' asked Mrs Wimpole, as soon as her husband come in through the door.

'Yes. But the pilot managed to bale out. No-one was hurt.'

'Thank God,' she said.

Mr Wimpole sat down heavily.

'I think we may be in for some more action, soon,' he said quietly.

'Why?' she asked.

'Well, the R.A.F. men didn't say much, but I got the feeling that this is the lull before the storm.'

The next day I saw Uncle Bob.

CHAPTER FOUR

It was quite late and I was sitting quietly knitting another scarf, hoping no-one would notice that it was well past my bedtime.

'Annie,' said Mr Wimpole, looking up from his newspaper, 'have you shut up the fowls?'
I blushed: 'No, I'm just going,' I said, getting up and going towards the door.
'You shouldn't leave it so late. It's almost dark; a fox might get them if you don't hurry.'

I took the big torch, put on my wellington boots, and went out. The chickens had been moved and they were now quite a way from the main farm buildings. I looked back; the house was in darkness, with every window covered with blackout material. Not a chink of light showed anywhere. I pointed the torch at the ground, as I'd been taught ("remember, any light is a target") and hurried up the track to the chicken houses.

I knew before I got there what had happened. There was a terrible fuss and squawking. I shone the torch on the ground and saw a mass of feathers, then I counted the chickens, as I did every night before I shut them up. There was no doubt; one was missing!

With a heavy heart, I put them to bed. I felt really bad; I knew I should have come earlier. It was the first time a chicken had been taken by a fox since I'd been looking after them.

I wandered round for bit, thinking that perhaps I was

wrong, perhaps the chicken had just got lost. I stood still and listened, in case it was clucking somewhere. The night was velvety dark now and there wasn't a sound.

Then I heard something. If I hadn't been listening out, I should have missed it. It was the faintest rustle, and it came from the small wood on top of the hill behind the chicken houses. I strained my ears; there it was again. Very very faint. Something was moving up in the wood.

'I bet that's the fox, enjoying the chicken,' I thought to myself, and turned back towards the farmhouse.

I walked back slowly, not wanting to tell the Wimpoles what had happened. I was nearly at the door when I heard the purr of an engine coming up the drive.

'Uncle Bob! It must be!'

Quickly, I snapped off my torch.

My eyes were used to the darkness and I could see the car crawling up towards the house. Very few people travelled by car nowadays; petrol was rationed and everyone saved up their petrol coupons for special occasions or emergencies. Even fewer people travelled at night. Car headlamps had to be shrouded with special covers with slits across them. These slits let out just enough light for the driver to see where he was going.

To my surprise, the car stopped at the top of the drive and didn't go any further. Three men got out and, very quietly, they started to unload some boxes. The boxes were obviously heavy because I could hear the men puffing with effort as they carried them round to the side door of the house. This door was seldom used by the family and it was usually kept locked, but, to my surprise, the men opened the door and disappeared inside. There were stairs there that led, via the back landing, up to the attic.

The three men came out of the side door again, then two of them got in the car, turned it round and drove back down the drive.

The other man stayed where he was, just outside the side door. He seemed to be waiting for someone. Then I saw him cup his hands over his mouth and the next moment I nearly dropped my torch with fright as the haunting cry of an owl drifted across the yard. Almost immediately the back door of the house opened and a beam of light showed, just for a second, as Mr Wimpole came out and picked his way carefully across to the man – who I was sure must be Uncle Bob.

I stood very still. I didn't know whether to run to the house or to stay where I was. The two men talked together in whispers for a few moments then, to my horror, Uncle Bob suddenly looked up and walked straight over to where I thought I was hidden.

He stopped in front of me and touched my arm:
'You must be Annie,' he said.

I swallowed. My mouth was dry and I found I couldn't speak. Uncle Bob frightened me. Even though I could hardly see him, I could feel his strength. He had moved so silently – almost gliding across the yard – and when he spoke again his voice was very quiet but full of authority:
'I'm told you can be trusted,' he said.

I nodded in the darkness.

'A lot may depend on you, Annie,' he went on. 'You do understand that no-one must know that I am here, don't you?'

I nodded again.

He took me by the shoulders and turned me towards him: 'You must promise me solemnly not to tell a soul you have seen me.'

His hands gripped my shoulders like a vice:
'I promise,' I whispered, finding my voice at last.

Mr Wimpole appeared beside him:
'Annie! What are you doing? I didn't see you there.'

'I was shutting up the chickens,' I stuttered. 'And the fox has got one. I'm very sorry.' I started to cry.

Mr Wimpole put his arm round me:
'Never mind Annie. That's the first time it's happened. Let it be a lesson to you.'

I nodded.

'I think I heard the fox, up in the wood,' I said.

Mr Wimpole smiled into the darkness: 'You're still not quite a country girl Annie,' he said. 'You'd never hear a fox; they're the quietest hunters in the world.'

'But I heard . . .'

'Now, no more chatter Annie. Go into the house and get to bed. And remember, not a word about this to anyone.'

I moved away:
'Goodnight,' I whispered. And my voice trembled.

'Goodnight Annie,' said Mr Wimpole.

But Uncle Bob said nothing.

It was strange, knowing that Uncle Bob was in the house, yet never seeing him. He must have spent a lot of time in his attic room. Once I caught a glimpse of him walking over the fields with a pair of binoculars round his neck.

As Mrs Wimpole had promised, he was never there when I brought a friend home to tea. It wasn't difficult to keep quiet about him; I often forgot he was living with us! But I dreamt about him; he was always there, at the back of my mind. Who was he? What was he doing?

Not long after my late night meeting with Uncle Bob, I was woken one night by an awful moaning noise. I sat up in bed and listened. It came from the bathroom, which was next to my bedroom, so I got out of bed and padded next door to see what was the matter.

I found one of the Land Army girls sitting on the edge of the bath clutching her stomach. She was white in the face.

'Annie,' she gasped. 'Go and fetch Mrs Wimpole. Quick.'

Mrs Wimpole came hurrying along to the bathroom, rubbing her eyes. She took one look at the poor girl and rang the doctor. Then she came back:
'Come along, my love,' she said. 'We'll take you straight to the doctor.' She bundled the poor girl up in a blanket and helped her to her feet.

'Can I come too?' I said. I'd never been out at night in the car.

'Oh, alright Annie, But don't wake the others. Quickly now.'

Mrs Wimpole got out the car and drove, as quickly as

she dared, down the farm drive and onto the road. The doctor lived in the next village. The road twisted and turned:

'Just as well I know the way, isn't it?' said Mrs Wimpole. There were no signposts; they had all been taken down early in the war to confuse any enemy that landed.

On the way out of the village, we had to stop at the roadblock and show our identity cards. We all had identity cards – grown-ups had green ones and we children had buff-coloured ones. You had to carry them with you wherever you went.

We got to the doctor's house and as soon as he saw the girl, he said he thought she should get straight to hospital – it was almost certainly appendicitis.

We did a lot of driving that night, but at last we were heading back up the road leading to the farm.

'I must have used a month's petrol ration,' said Mrs Wimpole. 'Never mind. I'm glad we had it to use. We are lucky, we are allowed more than most people.'

I was almost asleep; the drive had been long and very slow:

'Why's that?' I yawned.

'Because we live on a farm,' said Mrs Wimpole. 'We need extra for tractors and other farm machinery. Although we try and use the horses as much as ...'

'Look out!' I screamed. Suddenly I was wide awake.

Mrs Wimpole braked violently and I hit my head on the windscreen. A man had suddenly crossed the road ahead of us and, with the shrouded headlamps, we didn't see him until we were almost on him.

Mrs Wimpole stopped the car:

'Are you alright, Annie?'

'Yes. Just bumped.'

'Who on earth was that, out at this time of night?' she said.

'He had a lucky escape, whoever he was,' I said, rubbing my sore head.

It was very late when I finally tumbled into bed. But I couldn't sleep. I kept thinking about that man, running across the road at the bottom of the hill. Who was he – where was he coming from, or going to? Could he be anything to do with Uncle Bob? I tossed and turned but sleep wouldn't come, so I got out of bed and went to fetch a glass of water.

I got my water, then, not feeling sleepy any longer, I padded along the landing to the window. It was heavily covered with blackout material, but I lifted the corner a fraction and peered out. The moon was drifting in and out of clouds and everything was still. There was complete silence. I sipped my water, staring down at the peaceful shapes in the farmyard below, then I walked back towards my room.

I don't know what made me hesitate before I went back to bed. I stopped outside my door and listened, and it was only because everything else was so quiet that I heard anything. I strained my ears, wondering if I had imagined it. No! There it was again. A very very faint sound. Not an ordinary household noise but something strange, something I'd never heard before.

Part of me wanted to jump back into bed and pull the covers over my head and pretend I'd heard nothing. But the other part of me wanted to know what, or who, was making that noise.

I felt sure it must be coming from the attic. My heart started pounding, but I forced myself to creep very quietly along to the other end of the landing. Every footstep seemed noisy and heavy as I made my way cautiously along the floorboards in my bare feet. Once I trod on a squeaking board and it sounded like an explosion in the surrounding quietness.

At last I was at the foot of the attic stairs. A pale light shone from under the attic door and the strange noise was coming from inside. I crept up the stairs, one at a time, with infinite care, terrified that Uncle Bob would hear me. At the top, I knelt down and, as before, I peered through the keyhole.

Uncle Bob was sitting at a table, a lamp by his side. In front of him, on the table, was a bulky piece of equipment. He had headphones over his ears and his whole face was tense with concentration.

The sound I could hear was tapping.

Uncle Bob was tapping out something; something in code.

Although the night was warm, I shivered. Then, very quietly, I crept back to bed.

CHAPTER FIVE

The next morning Mrs Wimpole was speaking on the telephone as I came down to breakfast. After a few minutes, she replaced the receiver on the hook and came into the kitchen, looking serious:
'That was the hospital. She's doing well after the operation, but they say she won't be able to work on the farm for several months. We were short-handed as it was; now with harvest nearly on us, I don't know what we'll do.'

'I could help a bit more,' I said. 'I'm nearly ten.'

Mrs Wimpole smiled: 'Oh, I've already got lots of jobs for you to do in the holidays; but we really need a big strong lad to help with the harvest.'

Mr and Mrs Wimpole were deep in discussion as I left for school. Only two more days before the holidays. This would be my first summer holiday on the farm and I was really looking forward to it.

At playtime that morning I was surprised to see Mr Wimpole at the school, talking to the teacher. He patted me on the head before he left:
'See you at tea, Annie,' he said.

After school, I was chatting outside with my friends when some 'planes flew overhead. We didn't even look up – living near an airfield, the sound of aircraft was part of life. But the boys at school were much more interested. They spent most of their time either spotting 'planes or swopping army badges and buttons – or sometimes even the cardboard milkbottle tops which had flag designs on top. They looked up now:

'More Spitfires,' said one.

'Are they bombers?' I asked, not really interested.

Tommy Baxter heard and laughed.

'You're really stupid, Annie Foster,' he said. 'Don't you know anything? Spitfires are fighter' planes. They're the fighter 'planes from Duxford.'

'Oh, shut-up,' I said, 'you don't know everything.'

Tommy grinned:

'You'll have to be nice to me now, Annie,' he said.

'What?'

'You're going to see a lot of me in the holidays,' he went on.

'Why?'

'Because,' and he stopped for effect, 'I'm going to help on the farm.'

I could think of nothing to say. Big, bullying Tommy Baxter coming to spoil everything. I turned my head away. If he hadn't been watching, I think I would have cried.

• • • • •

We kept hearing on the wireless how the German Air Force (the Luftwaffe) were attacking the seaports and shipping in the channel. One evening I heard Mr Wimpole say:

'It's all leading up to an invasion. They're trying to force our 'planes to fight. They want to destroy our Air Force so they can invade.'

'Will they bomb the airfields, too?' said Mrs Wimpole.

Mr Wimpole nodded: 'It's only a matter of time,' he said.

Mr Wimpole was right. Very soon after this, in August 1940, we were plunged into the Battle of Britain. It was a terrible month for the R.A.F. The German Luftwaffe launched a massive attack on radar stations, airfields and aircraft factories, and "dogfights" as they were called, between our fighter 'planes and the German 'planes, took place in the skies all over south east England.

East Anglia was dotted with airfields – and Duxford, which was one of the most important – was only a few miles away from the farm.

But, at the time, I was only thinking of the summer holidays.

• • • • •

The first day of the summer holidays arrived – and with it Tommy Baxter and another lad. Tommy was just twelve, but he was big and strong. The other boy was sixteen, and he came from a family in the village.

To begin with, I went out of my way to avoid Tommy, but he was kept so busy he didn't have time to tease me.

The harvest began and everyone worked late. Mrs Wimpole felt sorry for Tommy, having to walk back to the village every evening:
'Why don't you stay here during the harvest, Tommy?' she said. 'We can find room for you somehow.'

Tommy was pleased; he'd settled down with his village family, but they didn't like his rude ways.

'All they like is the money they get for having me,' he said.

So, during harvest, Tommy became part of the household.

One of my jobs, during harvest-time, was to glean corn for my chickens from the newly cut fields. It was hot, hard, back-breaking work, but I didn't mind. I worked so hard that I managed to collect enough corn to feed them all through the following winter!

I had become very attached to the chickens – and I made sure I always shut them up in time. But, one day I noticed that one of my favourite hens was sick. I told Mrs Wimpole.

'Don't worry Annie,' she said. 'We always lose a few each year.'
But I did worry, and that evening, as I sat in the house, I couldn't settle:

'I'm just going to go and check on the sick hen,' I said.

Tommy, who was nearly asleep from his day's work, roused himself:
'I'll come with you,' he said.

It was very dark and, although I wished it wasn't Tommy, I was quite glad of company.

We made our way to the chicken houses and I checked my hen. She looked better, so, with relief, I shut them all up again.
As I started to walk away, Tommy said:
'What's that noise?'
We stood still. It was the same rustling noise I had heard before, and it came from the wood.
'Perhaps it's a fox,' said Tommy.
'Don't you know anything?,' I said. 'Foxes are silent hunters. You'd never hear a fox!'
For once, Tommy didn't have an answer. We walked back towards the house.

'There *was* something there,' said Tommy. 'If it wasn't a fox, what was it?'

I shivered, remembering the strange man whom we had nearly run over in the car. Could it be him? And was Uncle Bob involved? I remembered my promise to Uncle Bob and tried to change the subject, but Tommy persisted:

'You heard the noise, Annie, didn't you?'

I shrugged: 'It was only some bird or animal. Come on, let's get back.'

Tommy stopped and looked towards the wood again:

'I reckon there was someone up there,' he said.

'Don't be silly. Who'd be up there?' I wished Tommy would shut-up.

'I don't know, do I? But if there is someone up there I bet they're doing something fishy.'

'You read too many comics,' I said crossly.

'Come on, Annie. You heard the noise. Why don't we go up there and see?'

'Don't you dare!'

He laughed:

'See. You're scared. *You* think there's someone there, don't you?'

I suddenly longed to tell him about Uncle Bob, but I kept quiet. Instead I said:

'Why don't you tell the Wimpoles, then?'

Tommy shook his head:

'No, it's probably nothing. I'll go and take a look in the wood tomorrow – at dinner time when I have a break. D'you want to come?'

I nodded in the darkness. If Tommy did find anything, I wanted to be there; and it wouldn't be frightening in the daytime.

The next day was hot and still. Mr and Mrs Wimpole, the two remaining Land Army girls, the village boy and Tommy all started work early. I stayed behind in the house to make the picnic lunch. If the day was fine, we would all eat out in the fields at lunch-time, then we'd have a big meal in the evening, when everyone had stopped work. Sometimes they stayed out almost until dark.

I got busy spreading mountains of bread.

'Will they really eat all that, Annie?'

I jumped. I hadn't heard Uncle Bob come into the room. It was the first time I'd seen him in daylight. I suppose he knew that everyone else was working in the fields.

'Oh yes. Harvest-time's hungry work,' I said, licking the marge from my fingers.

'It's hard work for you, too,' he said. 'You're a real help on the farm.'

I blushed. But I was pleased.

I chatted on nervously. Uncle Bob made me uneasy: 'They get extra rations at harvest time,' I said. 'I have to share them all out.'

'They deserve them,' said Uncle Bob, absently.

He didn't say any more, but sat down at the table and started to read the newspaper. I asked him a question, but he didn't answer. He seemed distant and worried.

At last I finished the picnic. I washed my hands and headed for the door. Uncle Bob looked up:
'What are you going to do now?' he asked.

I was surprised he wanted to know:
'I've got to check all the water troughs, then I'm going to glean more corn for the hens.'

He nodded, then went back to reading his paper.

I walked out into the sunshine. After I'd checked the troughs, I went to a recently cut field and started picking up corn. The field was some way from the wood above the chicken houses, but I could see it from where I worked. Once or twice I glanced nervously towards it. Could there *really* be something (or someone) up there?

The sun rose steadily in the sky. After a couple of hours, I was hot, tired and thirsty, and my back ached from stooping. I stood up and stretched. Then I put the sack of collected corn over my shoulder and went back into the house to get the picnic.

I put the picnic into two baskets, then staggered out to the field at the bottom of the farm where the others were working. They'd made a lot of progress that morning and the neatly tied shocks of harvested corn were standing all over the field, drying in the hot sun. As I got closer, one of the Land Army girls saw me. She unharnessed the carthorses from the machinery and led them over to the trough for a drink. Mrs Wimpole came over and took the baskets from me:
'Well done, Annie,' she said.

Usually, I enjoyed these harvest picnics. We would spread out the food and drink in the shade of the hedge, then Mrs Wimpole would hand it round. There was always a lot of laughter and good-natured teasing while we ate, then everyone would lie back for half an hour for a well-earned rest.

But today I was jumpy, and even Mrs Wimpole noticed:

'You're very quiet, Annie,' she said, when everyone had finished eating.

'I'm just tired,' I said, glancing across at Tommy.

He took the hint and heaved himself to his feet:
'I'll help you pack up.'

He stuffed empty mugs and bottles into the baskets, then he put one basket on each arm and strode off. I trailed after him.

As soon as we were out of sight, he put down the baskets:
'Come on, I haven't got much time. We start again at two o'clock.'

He set a punishing pace up the hill past the chicken houses.

'Can they see us from the field?' I gasped, trying to keep up with him.

'No – no-one can see us,' he said.

'Except Uncle Bob,' I thought. He could easily see us from the attic.

At last we got to the edge of the wood, and Tommy started to crash through the undergrowth.

'Stop it, Tommy!' I said.

'Why?'

'Well, if there is anyone there, we don't want him to hear us.'

'Don't be daft. If anything fishy's going on, it won't be going on in broad daylight,' he said. But he trod more carefully after that.

Once we were inside the wood we felt rather stupid. It was quiet and still, except for the occasional birdsong. Sunlight filtered through the trees onto the brambles and moss beneath. It all seemed peaceful and innocent.

'What are we looking for?' I asked.

'Er ... wires, bits of metal, equipment,' said Tommy uncertainly.

For half an hour we searched, getting scratched and bad tempered but finding nothing except a few pieces of very old, very rusty farm machinery.

At last, Tommy stood up and stretched. Angrily, he pushed the hair away from his eyes with his hands: 'I can't stay any longer. They'll wonder where I am.'

He started off for the edge of the wood and I got up and followed him. We were both disappointed.
I thought, as I walked, about Uncle Bob, about the airfield, about the noise in the night. I wasn't looking where I was going.

Suddenly, I tripped and fell heavily, twisting my ankle.

Tommy looked round:
'Clumsy thing!' he said. Then, 'Are you alright?'

My ankle was very painful and I could feel the tears coming to my eyes. I sniffed and brushed them away. I wasn't going to let Tommy Baxter see me cry. I looked down at the ground to see what I'd tripped over. There was a loop of rusty wire sticking out of the earth; angrily I pulled at it.

The next moment I had forgotton about the pain in my ankle. For, as I'd pulled the wire, something started to lift up. The wire was attached to something!

I pulled harder and a square piece of wood came up towards me. It had been completely covered by earth, but it was loose earth which had recently been disturbed.

'Tommy, come here. Quickly. Look at this!'

Tommy lumbered over and crouched down beside me.

'What is it?'

'I don't know. I think it's a sort of lid. There might be something underneath.'

Very carefully, we scraped away the earth on top of the lid, then we lifted it up. Underneath, there was a hole, lined with bricks, and inside the hole there was something metal, protected by a waterproof covering.

Tommy put his hands inside the hole and lifted the package out. It was very heavy. Cautiously, he took off the waterproof covering.

'What is it?' I breathed.

Tommy sat back on his haunches: 'I think it's a transmitter.'

'A radio transmitter?'

He nodded. We looked at each other, wide-eyed.

'You were right, then,' I said, 'there *was* someone up here last night. What do you think they were doing?'

Tommy shrugged:
'Spying?'

His voice sounded matter-of-fact but his face was frightened. I'd never seen him look frightened before.

'Tommy, I'm scared. Let's go back and tell someone.'

For once, he didn't argue.

'OK. But we can't carry this thing. I'll put it back where it was.'

Together, we wrapped up the transmitter in the waterproof covering and put it back in the hole. We replaced the lid and carefully covered it up with the loose earth. When we'd finished, all that could be seen was the loop of rusty wire.

My heart was pounding. If there was a spy and he discovered us, what would happen? He could be nearby. We didn't know whether he came here in the daytime, too. I longed for the safety of the farmhouse and the company of the Wimpoles.

'Hurry up, Tommy. Let's get out of here,' I said.

Tommy rubbed his hands together to get rid of the earth, then he stood up:
'OK. Come on.'

We both turned to go and, as we did so, a twig snapped just behind us. I froze. Someone *was* there. Someone was watching us and had seen us discover the transmitter!

Tommy heard it too. He took my arm and propelled me forward:
'Come on – run!'

I started forward but then another voice spoke. A voice full of quiet authority. A voice I recognised:
'Not so fast! Stay right where you are.'

We both spun round. I was so frightened I found myself gripping Tommy's arm.

Then we saw him. In front of us now, with his arms

folded and a pair of binoculars round his neck.

It was Uncle Bob.

• • • • •

I was terrified. How could anyone creep up on us so quietly? Was Uncle Bob a spy? And if he was, what would he do to us?

Tommy broke away from me and started to run, but Uncle Bob was too quick for him. Tommy found himself held in an iron grip.

'Just a moment, young man,' he said. 'I want to talk to you both.'

Uncle Bob looked across at me and saw my frightened face. He smiled:
'Don't worry, Annie. I won't hurt you.'

He made us both sit on the ground and he squatted beside us. I was still shaking with fright and I could see that Tommy was close to tears.

'Stop shaking, Annie,' said Uncle Bob. 'I promise you that there's nothing to be afraid of. I'm not a German spy – far from it!'

'But wwhat were you ddoing here?' I stuttered.

Uncle Bob smiled:
'I can't tell you Annie. At least not until the war is over. And, in the meantime, I am going to have to trust you. Both of you.' He looked at us then and the smile left his face.

'This is very serious,' he said. Then he went on:
'If you tell anyone what you've just seen you could put a lot of people in a lot of danger.'

'How?' asked Tommy.

'The less you know, the better,' said Uncle Bob, standing up:

'Now,' he continued, 'will you both promise me not to say a word about what you found here just now?'

'I promise,' I whispered.

'OK,' said Tommy.

Uncle Bob nodded. He seemed satisfied.

He sighed: 'Thank you. Both of you. You have no idea what this means.'

'Didn't you know it was here?' I asked.

'No. I suspected it was somewhere on the farm,' said Uncle Bob. 'And, because of you, Annie, I thought it was probably up in this wood.'

'Because of me!'

Uncle Bob smiled:
'Yes, do you remember, on the night we met, you said you'd heard a fox in the wood?'

I nodded, then blushed and looked at Tommy. Uncle Bob didn't notice:

'Well, I came up here the next day. I went over the wood inch by inch. But I never found what I was looking for.'

'We only found it by accident. I tripped over the wire and twisted my ankle,' I said.

Uncle Bob smiled broadly:
'Well, Annie,' he said. 'You may have a twisted ankle – but because of it, you have probably saved hundreds of lives.'

'Now,' he said. 'This hasn't happened. Do you

understand? You have seen *nothing* up here.'

I opened my mouth to ask something but he held up his hand:
'No more questions. Off you go before someone misses you.'

He stared at us both for a moment, then he turned on his heel and walked away, hardly making a sound.

We made our way slowly back to the farm.

We never told another soul about what we'd seen in the wood.

CHAPTER SIX

The war dragged on for five dreary years. It seemed as if we had always been at war; I could hardly remember what life had been like before – back in our little house in Tottenham.

On August 16th, 1940, only a few days after our discovery in the wood, 220 high-explosive bombs fell in the Duxford area. As Mr Wimpole had guessed, the German Luftwaffe were trying to wipe out airfields and aircraft factories; I heard later that the factory where my Auntie Madge worked had been badly damaged about that time, too.

But a month later, in September 1940, the Luftwaffe started to attack London. The London blitz, it was called. Night after night I lay in bed and prayed that Mum was safe. Sometimes I climbed the hill behind the chicken houses after I'd shut up the hens. It was the highest point for miles around and from there you could sometimes see a glow in the sky over London, forty five miles away. In a country in total blackout, there was never any doubt what that glow meant.

'London got it bad again last night,' someone would say the next morning.

We had our fair share of bombs too – you could see fire bombs when they landed at night – they looked like jumping lights on the fields – and often the enemy 'planes returning from a bombing raid on London would get rid of their remaining bombs on their way to the coast; we had a few of those on the farm, too.

1941 was the worst year for air-raids on Cambridge. We were in and out of our air-raid shelters, at school and on the farm, all the time.

We were always raising money for something during the war. The people of Cambridgeshire managed to buy a new Spitfire for the R.A.F. and we did our bit by having a children's concert at the school. As well as helping buy weapons, we saved our pennies to send 'comforts' to the troops, to provide money for people made homeless by air-raids, for prisoners of war. It went on and on.

The Red Cross were always asking for games and books – for evacuees and wounded servicemen. I remember going through all the Wimpoles' cupboards and finding a mass of stuff to send.

Clothing became rationed and shoes were in very short supply. A lot of us living in the country started to wear wooden clogs.

Everywhere, there were uniforms. All the armed forces, of course, and the Home Guard, but also the light blue uniform worn by wounded servicemen and the drab uniforms with bright orange circles sewn on, worn by the Italian prisoners of war as they worked in the fields. There were American service uniforms, too.

The Americans came into the war in 1941 and some were stationed not far away, at Debden. Mrs Wimpole managed to get permission to have a weekly dance for local girls and some of these young men, and this took place in Saffron Walden. Our Land Army girls were thrilled. I remember them coming back to the farm after these dances and sharing out the precious bars of chocolate they'd been given by the Americans.

In June 1943, Duxford airfield was handed over to the United States Army Air Force, so the Americans were everywhere. I remember, at Christmas that year, they gave the village children a wonderful party; for the first time in years, every child had a bar of chocolate; the men had gone without a month's rations themselves, so we could have a good Christmas!

At last, on May 8th, 1945 (VE Day) the war in Europe was over! We had a huge village party and a bonfire on the recreation ground. There was so much happiness, but a lot of sadness, too.

I was lucky. Nearly everyone in my family survived the war. But I felt the sadness of others. One of the Wimpoles' sons was killed in action; so was the brother of one of our Land Army girls. And Tommy Baxter suffered most. His father was killed in the fighting and his mum was killed during the\London blitz. I shall never forget the pain on his face when he heard about his mum.

• • • • •

And what of Uncle Bob? He disappeared as silently as he had arrived and, until the other day, I never saw him again.

Then, just a few months ago, he was interviewed on television. He is a very old man now and I hardly recognised him. Only now do I know his real name and how much he did, quietly and unobtrusively, to protect this country in the war.

I found out where he lived and I went to see him. Then, at last, I discovered the truth about his presence on the farm in 1940.

For some time vital, secret information from the East Anglian airfields was being sent to the Germans. There was a highly organised spy ring and the leader of the spy ring lived near Duxford. He was in constant touch with the enemy, using the radio transmitter we found in the wood.

Uncle Bob was sure that the spy could pass as an Englishman and that he was trusted by our side which was why he could get hold of this secret information. Uncle Bob's job was to find out the name of the spy and then make sure he was being fed the *wrong* information. He did find out the man's name – and he managed to tap into the spy's transmissions with the high-powered radio equipment he had in our attic. For several more months, the spy kept up his work, not knowing that he was being given wrong information. Because of Uncle Bob's work – and because of our discovery – many lives were saved.

• • • • •

You may wonder how I can remember so much about my wartime childhood. I was only nine when I met Uncle Bob and when Tommy and I discovered the transmitter in the wood.

Well, the answer is simple. I have someone with me who jogs my memory from time to time; when I forget something, he remembers.

Tommy Baxter and I were married in 1952 and, despite a lot of quarrels, we have had a very happy life together!

PLACES TO VISIT

The Imperial War Museum, Duxford,
Cambridgeshire

The Imperial War Museum, Lambeth Road,
London SE1

HMS Belfast (London's Floating Naval Museum)
Simon's Wharf, Vine Lane, Tooley Street,
London SE1

Cabinet War Rooms, Clive Steps,
King Charles Street, London SW1

The Muckleburgh Collection, Weybourne,
Nr Sheringham, Norfolk.